SUS-PECKS

150

125

100

75

50

0

-PECKS

1B

BIRD

THE USUAL SUS-PECKS

THE BLUES

A.K.A. Jim, Jake & Jay

THE USUAL SUS-PECKS

MATILDA

A.K.A. THE WHITE BIRD

ANGRY BIRDS™

CONTENTS

ROVIO

Pedigree®

Published 2012. Pedigree Books Ltd, Beech Hill House, Walnut Gardens, Exeter, Devon EX4 4DH
books@pedigreegroup.co.uk • www.pedigreebooks.com
The Pedigree trademark, email and website addresses, are the sole and exclusive properties
of Pedigree Group Limited, used under licence in this publication.

£7.99

JOIN THE ANGRY BIRDS FLOCK

Welcome to remote but picturesque Piggy Island, home to a flock of rare and exceptionally angry birds. Why so mad? Did they get out of the nest on the wrong side? Did they just hatch that way? No! If left in peace the birds would no doubt live happily ever after. Unfortunately, the birds are not the island's only inhabitants....

The Flock has to deal with the ever-present threat posed by the Kingdom of the Pigs, presided over by the greedy King Pig who has but one, evil aim - to find the birds' eggs and eat them. The birds only have three eggs and faced with this constant threat to the very survival of their flock, they are, of course, angry. Well, wouldn't you be?

6

A message from Red...

Golden eggs are hidden throughout this annual. You'll need to find all 21 of them and then put them in the right pecking order to unlock the secret message on the last page of the book.

So come on, get going; remember *'the early bird catches the pig!'*

Turn the page to support the birds' cause and join the Flock!

RED

A.K.A.
the Red Bird

Highly angry!

Red is the formidable leader of the Angry Birds. Despite his seniority and his capacity to inspire the Flock, Red is physically one of the weaker birds.

Special markings

Red sees it as his ultimate duty to see the eggs hatched. When this is achieved he will return to the freedom he enjoyed in his youth.

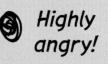

Fans' nicknames for Red: Boss Red, Wood Breaker

Likes
Motivating his flock
Hates
The burden of leadership

In the game

Red has no special abilities when tapped which means that although he is able to cause great damage to weaker structures, he does struggle to shatter more than one long wood or glass block, per flight. However, he is very useful throughout the levels and episodes because he can be used to finish off areas which have been weakened by other members of the Flock.

Always on the look out!

Ca-caw!

Powers:	Strong Leader
Gender:	Male
Locations:	Most Levels
Strength:	Average
Height:	100 BMUs (Bird Measurement Units)

9

ADD TO THE ANGER!

The Angry Birds would always welcome additional members to the Flock, especially when there's a long day of aerial attacks ahead.

Use the opposite page to create a new Angry Bird and the space below to describe its character, attributes and powers.

SQUAWK!

10

MY BIRD IS CALLED

FACT FILE

Its nickname is...

It measures... (BMUs):

Its feathers are...

It likes...

It doesn't like...

Its ABFF (Angry Bird Friend Forever) is...

When launched it can...

It also...

PICNIC PANIC

The Angry Birds need eyes in the back of their heads when greedy pigs are around. Do you share their powers of observation and memory?

Grab a watch or egg timer and give yourself 60 seconds to check out this picture of the birds attempting to enjoy a picnic. You'll need to take in every teeny tiny detail, because when the minute's up you must cover the picture and see how many of the questions below you can answer correctly.

Questions

1. Is Bomb in the picture?

2. How many Angry Birds are in the picture?

3. Is Red's beak open or closed?

7. On which side of the picture are the pigs?

8. Of what kind are the pigs in the picture?

9. If the picnic is in the birds' nest, where are the eggs?

4. Besides fruit and baked goods, which edible item is in the nest?

....

5. What are the two non-edible objects in the nest?

....

6. How many strawberries are in the nest?

....

10. How many flowers are shown in the picture?

....

11. What colours are the flowers?

....

12. How many of the pigs are grinning?

....

13

CHUCK

A.K.A. the Yellow Bird

Fans' nicknames for Chuck:

Lazer Bird, Speedy Bird

Streamlined Physique →

Likes
Playing practical jokes on the Flock

Hates
Failing or being defeated

Friend and confidante of Red, hyperactive show-off Chuck trains constantly for forthcoming missions. However his lack of concentration means he's forever changing training routines.

Yellow is never slow!

Powers:	In-Flight Acceleration
Gender:	Male
Locations:	Many
Strength:	Normal
Height:	115 BMUs
	(Bird Measurement Units)

In the game

Chuck is, without doubt, the fastest of the Angry Birds. His intense speed, augmented by his special power – triggerable acceleration - means he causes great damage to both the pigs and their structures. Much like the other birds, Chuck's success depends on the block and the angle at which he strikes it, but he is particularly useful when used on wooden obstacles and is able to penetrate several walls in one move.

Great with wooden structures!

FINISH THE FLOCK

Phew! A rare and welcome moment of respite for the birds before the assault on thieving pigs.

Join the dots to finish the Flock and then colour them all in using your brightest shades.

Squawk!

DROP IT LIKE IT'S HOT!

SPOT THE

Bbbbrrrr! It's freezing and the pigs have dug in for the winter! With so much snow and ice around it's hard for the birds, but their frustration just makes them angrier and more determined than ever.

DIFFERENCE

There are 10 differences between
Picture A and Picture B.

Can you find them all?

19

I'LL SHOW YOU WHO NEEDS
ANGER MANAGEMENT!!!!!!!!!

BOMB

A.K.A. **the Bomb Bird**

Likes
Planning schedules and sticking to a routine

Hates
Deviating from the above in any way

WARNING!
May explode at any moment!

Fans' nicknames for Bomb:
Kamikaze Bird, Stone Smasher

Bomb is a tense bird with a terrible temper, which flares frequently. As a result he is rather a loner. When the pigs hit the fan however, he is fearless and quick to act.

Tic...

Tic...

Tic...

BOOM!!

Do you feel lucky, pig?

Known as Bomb, due to his awesome ability to explode and incinerate anything in his vicinity, the Black Bird is the most powerful of the Angry Birds. He glows red on contact with a target and explodes moments later, causing heavy damage to objects in close range and weakening or moving things within a larger radius, due to the shockwave created by his disintegration. His powers are triggerable and employed by tapping the screen or clicking the mouse.

Powers: Ability to Explode

Gender: Male

Locations: Many

Strength: Tough/Strong

Size: 135 BMUs
(Bird Measurement Units)

So, you want to join the Flock. Sadly, you're no use to them if you're a placid type, so Red's right-hand bird, Chuck has devised this simple chart to help you work out where you rate on the anger scale. Read each situation and if it makes your blood boil then follow the 'yes' arrow. Follow 'no' if you think you wouldn't necessarily blow your top.

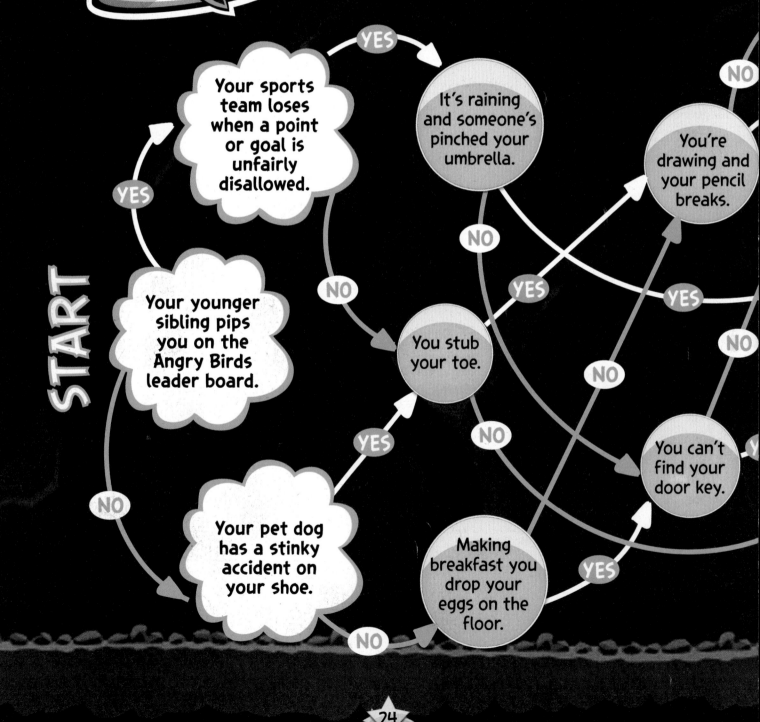

START

Your sports team loses when a point or goal is unfairly disallowed.

YES

Your younger sibling pips you on the Angry Birds leader board.

It's raining and someone's pinched your umbrella.

NO

YES

NO

You're drawing and your pencil breaks.

NO

NO

YES

You stub your toe.

YES

NO

NO

YES

You can't find your door key.

NO

YES

Your pet dog has a stinky accident on your shoe.

Making breakfast you drop your eggs on the floor.

YES

NO

ARE YOU?

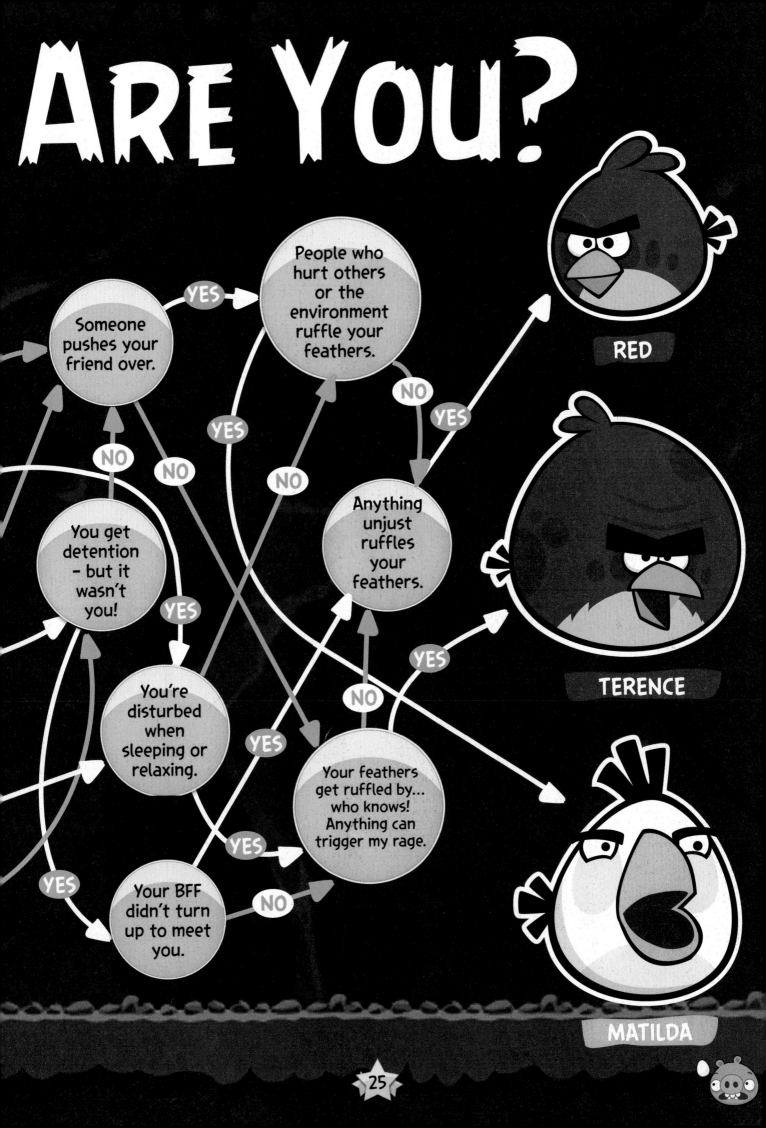

Someone pushes your friend over.

YES → People who hurt others or the environment ruffle your feathers.

NO

YES

NO

You get detention – but it wasn't you!

YES

YES

NO

NO

Anything unjust ruffles your feathers.

NO

YES

You're disturbed when sleeping or relaxing.

YES

YES

Your feathers get ruffled by... who knows! Anything can trigger my rage.

YES

NO

YES

Your BFF didn't turn up to meet you.

RED

TERENCE

MATILDA

STENCIL A TEE

You'll be the best-dressed bird on the block with this totally cool t-shirt!

1. CUT ALONG THE DOTTED LINE ON THE OPPOSITE PAGE TO REMOVE THE PAGE WITH THE SLOGAN FROM THE BOOK.

3. Tape your paper stencil to the thick piece of card using masking tape and use it as a template to cut out a sturdier stencil from the card.

2. Using a craft knife or scissors, carefully cut out all the black areas so you're left with holes – make sure you lean on a piece of cardboard while you do this, so that you don't scratch or mark the surface of the table.

6. CAREFULLY PEEL AWAY THE STENCIL AND ALLOW THE PAINT TO DRY.

4. TAPE THE CARD STENCIL TO THE FRONT OF YOUR T-SHIRT WITH MASKING TAPE.

5. Now, paint the holes in the stencil using a stencil brush or a dense foam roller, making sure you've generously covered all the holes.

Knives and scissors are sharp and irons are hot! Always ask an adult to help when crafting.

SQUAWK!

I'M AN ANGRY BIRD

I'M AN ANGRY BIRD

Some fabric paints need fixing using an iron. Follow the paint manufacturers' instructions and always ensure you place a tea towel over the paint to stop it sticking to the iron.

CA-CAW!

27

MATILDA

A.K.A.
the White Bird

Immaculate plumage!

Fans' nicknames for Matilda

Egg Master,

Chicken Bird

Kindhearted Matilda tries to find a peaceful solution for everything – she even brews herbal teas to keep Bomb calm.

She dreams of the birds and pigs living in harmony but in the meantime, her passion for protecting all living things ensures she's fully behind every mission to safeguard the eggs.

Likes
Practicing Nest Shui to make a tranquil nesting environment

Hates
Anything or anyone – including herself - who harms fauna or flora

Powers: Drops Egg Bombs

Gender: Female

Locations: Many

Strength: Weak (prior to egg launch) / Medium (after launch)

Size: 140 BMUs
(Bird Measurement Units)

Drop it like it's hot!

In the game

Matilda's role is to wreak havoc on the pigs with her Egg Bombs, which she unleashes whenever she loses her temper. Matilda's Egg Bomb bombardments terrify the pigs and her Egg Bombs are indeed powerful, but their short blast radius limits the amount of destruction they can bring about to a wider area.

↑

Calming beverage!

W

ODE TO A BIRD...

Can you work out which characters are being described in these Piggy Island Poems?

Use the rhymes to help you fill the gaps, which should, in turn, help you reveal the birdy subject.

I'm a cute bird it's true,
With my plumage so bright,
And my body so small.
I look superb -- ------.
I'm weaker than most,
But when I'm in the sky.
My special power means,
I -------- !

Who am I?--- -----.

I'm porcine and brave,
From my snout to my trotter.
Bird lovers may claim,
I'm a bit of a ------.
But I do my duty,
Commanding the ----.
I'm -------- ---,
Patriotic but barmy.

I'm bright and I'm speedy,
A wired little fellow.
You'll see me fly past and,
My feathers are ------.
But get on my wrong side,
You'll be out of ----;
'Cause I can wreak havoc,
For my name is ------.

WORD BANK

multiply
luck
rotter
the blues
yellow
corporal pig
in flight
army
chuck

THE ANGRIEST SNACK AROUND

What a cheese-tastic version of Red! This angry snack looks and tastes amazing, plus it's really quick to make because it doesn't involve any cooking. Bonus!

You'll need an adult to help with cutting out Red's features, but even the simplest minion pig could then assemble Red on the plate.

YOU WILL NEED:

- Bag of mini round cheeses in red wax wrappers
- Pack of slices of yellow-coloured processed cheese
- Pack of slices of white-coloured cheese (Edam or cheddar)
- Nori sheets (the edible seaweed used to wrap sushi) OR black olives
- A sharp knife

HERE'S WHAT YOU DO:

1. Carefully cut the bottom segment of red wrapper from the circle – leaving the cheese intact (as in illustration).
2. Cut two red top feathers from the piece of red wax wrapper you have just removed, lace the two red feathers on the plate and rest the cheese on top.
3. Now cut small two round circles from the white slice of cheese for the eyes and a beak shape from the slice of yellow cheese and place on the bird's body as shown.
4. Cut five small strips from the Nori, or olives and place three beneath and to the left side of the cheese to form tail feathers, and two above the eyes, for brows.

SQUAWK!

Knives are sharp. Ask a grown-up to help you.

Great Eggspectations

TERENCE

A.K.A.
Big Brother

Socially awkward Terence is the quietest of the Flock and his only form of communication is his disconcerting stare. He can get a pig to confess plans or down tools, just by looking at him.

Unfortunately, Terence has little control over his destructive power and consequently the other birds are wary of him and do not want him near the eggs.

Fans' nicknames for Terence:

Hulk, Fat Bird

Likes
Sleeping with his face against the ground

Hates
Pigs – he is immediately enraged by the mere sight of them

In the game

Despite his bulk, Terence is capable of stealth and will appear quite suddenly and without warning. His immense size and level of fury mean he is a wrecking ball in bird-form who consistently wreaks destruction on even the most sturdily built pig stronghold.

Be afraid... be very afraid!

Powers:	**Immense Size and Momentum**
Gender:	**Male**
Locations:	**Many**
Strength:	**Strong**
Size:	**Over 175 BMUs** (Bird Measurement Units)

FRUITY FEATHERS

This fruit-freshing dessert will have you shaking your tail feathers like a member of the Flock after a particularly successful bombardment.

YOU WILL NEED:

- Large watermelon
- Cucumber
- I gala or honeydew melon
- Purple grapes

There's no cooking required, but you will need help carving the fruit to make the bird's facial features. It's irritatingly good for you – so you may want to add an egg-shaped dollop of ice cream. Mmmmm!

1 Cut a large, inch thick, circular slice from the melon. Place on the plate.

2 Cut two slices of cucumber and place on the melon as eyes.

36

3

Cut one grape in half and place one half on each eye, as the pupils.

SQUAWK!

Remember to ask a grown-up to help you to carve the fruit Knives are sharp.

4

Cut another grape into five segments to make the eyebrows and tail feathers.

5

Cut three extra chunks from the red flesh of the remaining watermelon. Place above the head as feathers.

6

Carve a chunk from the Gala melon for the yellow beak. Place the beak on the face and voila! One fruity-feathered fried.

THE SLINGSHOT IS YOURS...

Don't you just love watching those birds ping into the blue and soar majestically through the air until KABOOOOM! Destructo!

Another piggy fortress crumbles to dust. Surely you could do better than Moustache Pig and his minions when it comes to building indestructible hide-outs? We've had some minions lay the foundations but now it's up to you!

READY, BIRDY, GO.....

SPOT THE PIGGY POOPER!

It's Christmas and the pigs are having a party,
but one of the pigs isn't wearing his Santa hat.

Can you spot the odd one out? When you've
found the piggy pooper, encircle him with your
pen or pencil in a 'ring of shame'.

THE BLUES

A.K.A.
Jim, Jake and Jay

Hatched from the same egg The Blues are still very naïve and often get into trouble. Blues dream of becoming champion pig-slayers like Red.

Fans' nicknames for The Blues: Cluster Birds

Likes
Imitating the other birds and making up new and exciting games

Hates
Being scolded or ignored

Powers:	Ability to Split into Three Birds
Gender:	Male
Locations:	Most Levels
Strength:	Average (when deployed as a trio)
Size:	75 BMUs
	(Bird Measurement Units)

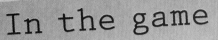

In the game

The Blues' unique power comes with their ability to launch as one but then split into three on impact or when triggered.

This quirk allows them to target several obstacles at once. Their diminutive size means they are used to weaken rather than destroy obstacles, but they wield special strength against glass, ice and snow.

Triple Threat!

Destroyers of glass, ice and snow! →

THE BIG BIRDIE QUIZ
PART 1

BE PREPARED TO HAVE YOUR FEATHERS RUFFLED!
It's quiz time! Will you rule the roost, or are you a total birdbrain when it comes to answering questions about the Angry Birds? We've started you off gently; you only have to answer 'True' or 'False', so you have a 50% chance of getting it right each time.
Don't forget to check your answers on page 77.

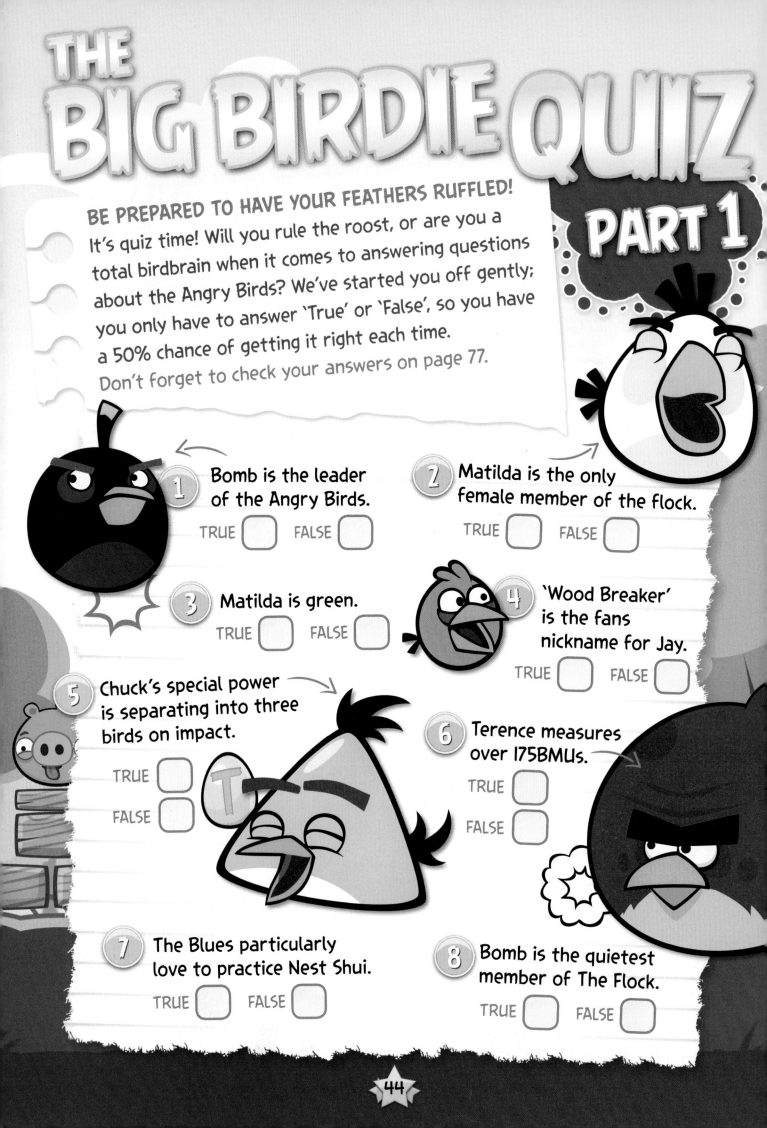

1 Bomb is the leader of the Angry Birds.

TRUE ☐ FALSE ☐

2 Matilda is the only female member of the flock.

TRUE ☐ FALSE ☐

3 Matilda is green.

TRUE ☐ FALSE ☐

4 'Wood Breaker' is the fans nickname for Jay.

TRUE ☐ FALSE ☐

5 Chuck's special power is separating into three birds on impact.

TRUE ☐
FALSE ☐

6 Terence measures over 175BMUs.

TRUE ☐
FALSE ☐

7 The Blues particularly love to practice Nest Shui.

TRUE ☐ FALSE ☐

8 Bomb is the quietest member of The Flock.

TRUE ☐ FALSE ☐

9 Terence likes to sleep with his head under Matilda's wing?

TRUE ☐   FALSE ☐

10 The pig who wears a helmet serves as foreman of the Minions and oversees the building of the fortresses.

TRUE ☐   FALSE ☐

11 King Pig's egg stash is empty.

TRUE ☐   FALSE ☐

H

12 The pigs and the Angry Birds live on Battle Island.

TRUE ☐   FALSE ☐

Do we live on Battle Island?

13 The birds only have four known eggs, which they protect at all times.

TRUE ☐   FALSE ☐

14 A common Angry Bird call is 'ch-cheep!'

TRUE ☐   FALSE ☐

15 Chuck has a triangular body shape.

TRUE ☐   FALSE ☐

Go to **page 62** for Part 2 of the quiz

What's the matter piggies...

can't take a yolk?

THE PIGS

The Kingdom of The Pigs is located on Piggy Island and is ruled by the devious and greedy King Pig – identifiable only by his crown and haughty manner. Unfortunately for the Angry Birds who share the island, King Pig is obsessed with eating the Angry Birds' eggs and has decreed that his loyal subjects must hunt them down at all costs. Here's a guide to who's who in the drift!

Trick or treat!

KING PIG

Role:
Undisputed leader of the pigs

Other Oinkfo:
King Pig is respected by the other pigs who believe he has a huge supply of eggs. Lives in mortal dread they will discover his egg stash, which is in fact, completely empty.

MOUSTACHE PIG

Role:
Foreman of the Minion pigs

Other Oinkfo:
Sadly, this stubborn and domineering pig is lacking in any real skill when it comes to the engineering of pig fortresses, which are usually on the verge of collapsing even before bird bombardment.

CORPORAL PIG

Role:
Commander of the Pig Army

Other Oinkfo:
Corporal Pig is brave and patriotic. Unfortunately, he is unable to lead more than four pig soldiers at one time.

MINION PIGS

Role:
Lowly Subjects of King Pig

Other Oinkfo:
Minion Pigs are obedient, hardworking and always follow orders from their superiors. They do their best to find eggs for their monarch and under their foreman's guidance they build all manner of structures.

HIDE & SQUEAK

The pigs have been left reeling by the Angry Birds' latest bombardment and their belongings are all over the place.

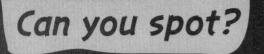

- A bell
- A wrapped gift
- A pickaxe
- King pig's spare crown
- A pit helmet
- A spade

- Some precious stones
- A cake
- A candle
- A balloon
- A broken cauldron
- A four leafed clover
- A pile of gold coins

KING PIG COLOUR COPY

He's powerful, he's portly and he's permanently hungry.
Love him or hate him, you can't ignore King Pig.

Now's your chance to create a majestic masterpiece of your own. Just draw the details from each square of the grid on the left, into the corresponding square in the empty grid on the right hand page.

Then grab your most lurid green pens or pencils to bring him to life. Long Live the King!

THE ANGRY BIRDS IN SPACE

They're still the angriest birds on the planet, but now they're also the angriest birds in the universe. Yes, the Angry Birds have entered another galaxy and now they're superheroed up and ready to go.

MEET THE SPACE BIRDS!

Check out Red's super sleek mask and the cool new look. But he's still good old, reliable Red.

In space, the Blues split into three with an accompanying flash of lightning and a rumble of thunder.

The bird the others followed into space has amazing powers. He can turn different elements into ice.

A supercharged version of The Bomb, Space Bomb Bird is particularly proud of his superhero cape, which is adorned with the Angry Birds Egg Brooch. Nice!

In space, Terence is green. Just don't confuse him with the pigs or he'll blow his top!

Chuck has cool laser glasses in space. His laserbeam allows him to home in on any target and reduce wood to splinters in a nano-second.

Use the pictures of the birds to guide you, as you colour in the brilliant space scene below!

PIGS IN SPACE

The Space Birds' intergalactic rivals look very similar to their old earth-based adversaries. Only now they often need special equipment like bubble helmets and antennae, in order to be able to breathe and communicate. Plus, in freezing temperatures they can literally turn blue with cold.

Can you bring these Space Pigs, to life with green pens and pencils? As you can see, the poor old Minions are so cold they have icicles dripping from their snouts, so you'll need shades of bbbrrrrrrrrilliant blue for them.

IN SPACE NO-ONE CAN HEAR YOU OINK!

Oh no! This poor Minion Pig was so busy egg-dreaming
that he has accidentally floated off from his group.
Can you steer him safely back through the cluster of asteroids?

SPACE SEARCH

There are ten words relating to the Angry Birds in Space, hiding in the grid below.

Can you find each of the words in this list and locate it in the grid?

- **ANTENNA**
- **ASTEROID**
- **BUBBLE**
- **CAPE**
- **EGG BROOCH**
- **ICICLES**
- **LASERBEAM**
- **MOON**
- **ROCK**
- **WORMHOLE**

O	C	A	P	I	A	N	N	T	E	N	A
O	I	C	I	A	S	T	R	O	D	S	S
M	A	E	B	R	E	S	A	L	V	E	T
O	S	W	E	E	E	E	W	O	H	S	E
M	T	M	L	L	S	G	Y	C	B	U	R
N	R	H	C	B	R	N	O	A	R	P	O
B	O	I	E	B	O	O	J	P	O	E	I
U	C	T	R	U	R	B	C	E	O	R	D
I	D	O	Y	B	U	R	A	K	H	H	K
B	W	N	G	N	B	M	O	O	N	E	O
L	O	G	A	S	B	A	N	T	E	R	C
E	E	L	O	H	M	R	O	W	O	O	R

We've hidden an eleventh word in the grid. It's not listed but here's a clue; it's something to do with the way we birds look in space!
When you've found it, cross it off and then write it in the space below.

_____

59

COMIC CAPERS

As Another day dawned on Piggy Island...

Ever fancied sending King Pig on a wild goose chase, seeing Bomb and Terence playing 'chicken', or seeing how Halloween pans out on Piggy Island? Well, now is your chance. These pages have been designed especially for you to create an Angry Birds comic strip. You're free to dream up your very own story, so let your imagination fly!

THE END

THE BIG BIRDIE QUIZ

PART 2

DING DING. SECOND ROUND.
Time for Part 2 of the quiz and the opportunity to find out if you've really been paying attention. Will you fly like a bird or sink like a pig in a swamp? When you're done, turn to page 77 for the answers.

1 The two Angry Birds mixed up in this picture are:

A Chuck and Jay

B Red and Terence

C Terence and Matilda

2 The Blues are particularly useful...

A In snowy or icy weather

B To hit more than one obstacle at a time

C Both of the above

3 Egg Bombs are dropped by...

A Bomb

B Red

C Matilda

4 One of Terence's quirks is that he...

A Only communicates by staring

B Was brought up among the pigs – before defecting

C Is a great cook

5 The extreme close up has captured...

A Terence B Red C Chuck

6 What colour is Moustache Pig's facial hair?

A Brown

B Black

C Blonde

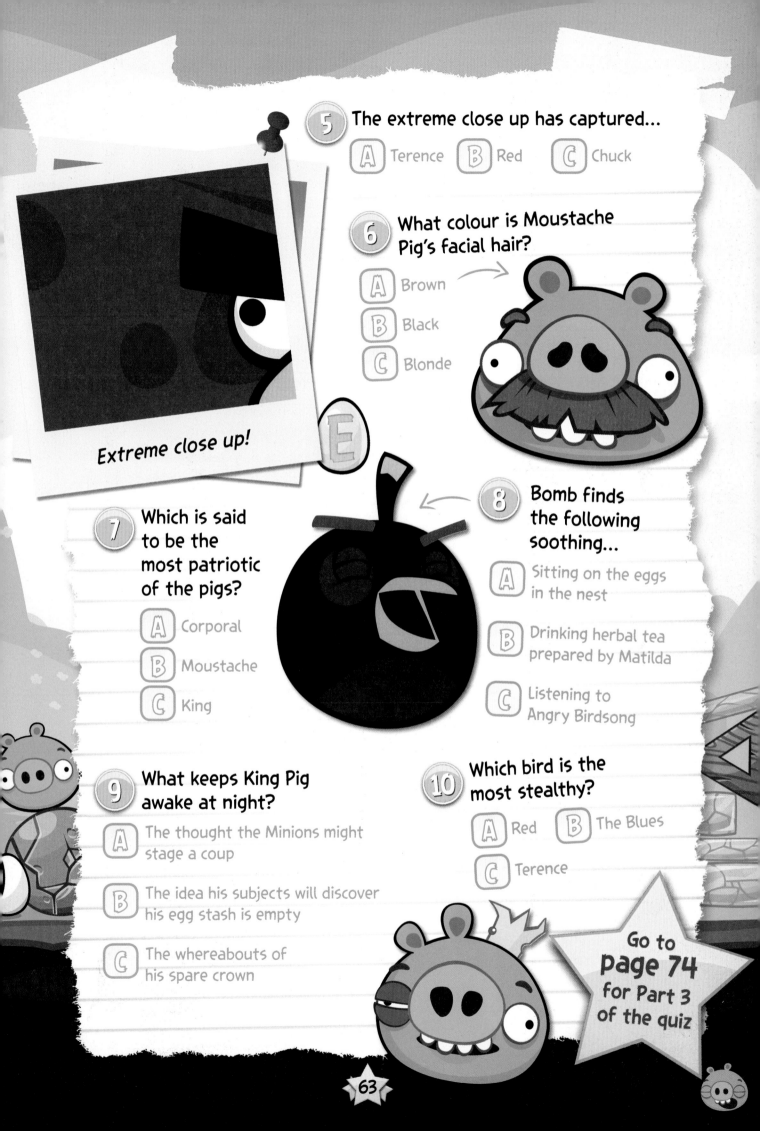

Extreme close up!

E

7 Which is said to be the most patriotic of the pigs?

A Corporal

B Moustache

C King

8 Bomb finds the following soothing...

A Sitting on the eggs in the nest

B Drinking herbal tea prepared by Matilda

C Listening to Angry Birdsong

9 What keeps King Pig awake at night?

A The thought the Minions might stage a coup

B The idea his subjects will discover his egg stash is empty

C The whereabouts of his spare crown

10 Which bird is the most stealthy?

A Red B The Blues

C Terence

Go to **page 74** for Part 3 of the quiz

CARVE A PIG PUMPKIN

It's Halloween – night of ghostly goings-on, when Angry Birds haunt the skies and petrified piggies tremble inside their spooky and tumbledown fortresses. But you can light the night outside your house with this fab pig pumpkin. It's simple to make and looks scarily realistic!

You Will Need:

- One carving pumpkin
- Black marker pen
- Tools for carving – either a sharp knife or a keyhole saw; barbeque skewer
- An ice cream scoop
- A tea light for the inside

1. Cut the lid of the pumpkin off using the knife or keyhole saw.

2. Scoop the flesh and seeds out using the ice cream scoop.

SQUAWK!

Pumpkin carving requires very sharp tools. Get a grown-up to help! We don't want a gruesome accident.

3. Copy the features shown above onto the side of the pumpkin in black marker pen. Cut the eyes, eyebrows, mouth and snout out to create the pig's face.

4. Light the tea light and place it in the pumpkin. Put the lid on and display.

PIGGY FASHION

Corporal Pig's helmet has a dual functionality. It affords him extra protection from bird bombardments while lending him an air of authority, which, he believes, sets him apart from he Minion Pigs.

He's a practical creature, focused on his duty and not given to flights of fancy, but he sometimes wishes he could add some stylish piggy touches to his attire. Can you help out by designing some hot headgear for him? Think motivating mottos, army slogans and piggy colour schemes.

THROW AN ANGRY
BIRD-DAY PARTY

ANGRY INVITES

Check out this cool Angry Birds invitation. You could use this example to invite all your friends to your party.

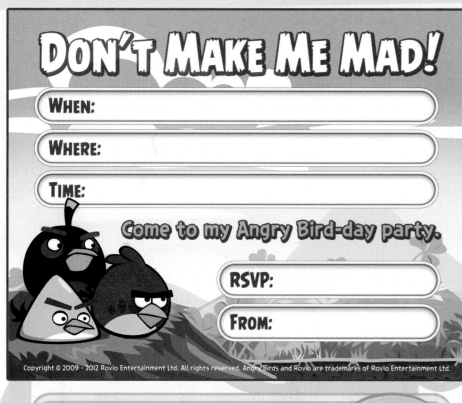

DON'T MAKE ME MAD!

WHEN:

WHERE:

TIME:

Come to my Angry Bird-day party.

RSVP:

FROM:

PIG CAN ALLEY

There are loads of games you could play at your party, such as 'pin the feathers on the bird' (pin the tail on the donkey) or 'pass the piggy' (passing pig balloons to each other without using your hands).

This pig-based twist on a tin can alley is brilliant fun. Your guests will be lining up to bombard those pesky porkers.

FOR PIG CAN ALLEY

YOU WILL NEED:

- 6 empty and clean tin cans
- I red rubber or plastic ball
- Multi-surface acrylic craft paints in green, yellow, red, white and black
- Paintbrushes
- Black permanent marker pen
- The piggy face (template A) and bird face (template B)

HERE'S WHAT YOU DO:

I. Paint your cans green and allow to dry

2. Hold template A onto the can and carefully draw round it with the pen

3. Paint in the features and allow to dry before repeating on the other cans

4. Hold template B to the ball and draw around it. Paint in features and allow to dry.

5. When you're ready pile the cans up, three on the bottom, two in the middle and one on top and take turns trying to knock them down with Red!

Want to throw the ultimate bird-day party? Read on to discover how to theme your do, giving everything from the invites to the party favours an Angry twist.

PARTY FAVOURS

Buy coloured paper party bags in red and green and use the templates C and D from pages 70-71, to create Angry Bags. Fill them with tiny gifts and a piece of your Angry Birds cake.

SQUAWK!

Don't forget to make the Angry Bird cake on page 72 and serve up some of the delicious snacks and recipes on pages 31 and 36.

BONKERS BALLOONS

YOU WILL NEED:
- Green Balloons
- Red Balloons
- Double sided sticky tape
- Scissors

HERE'S WHAT YOU DO:

Photocopy or scan in templates C and D (on pages 70-71) and print out as many copies of them as you have balloons. Now cut around them and tape Red's face to the red balloons and King Pig's features to the green balloons.

TEMPLATE A

TEMPLATE B

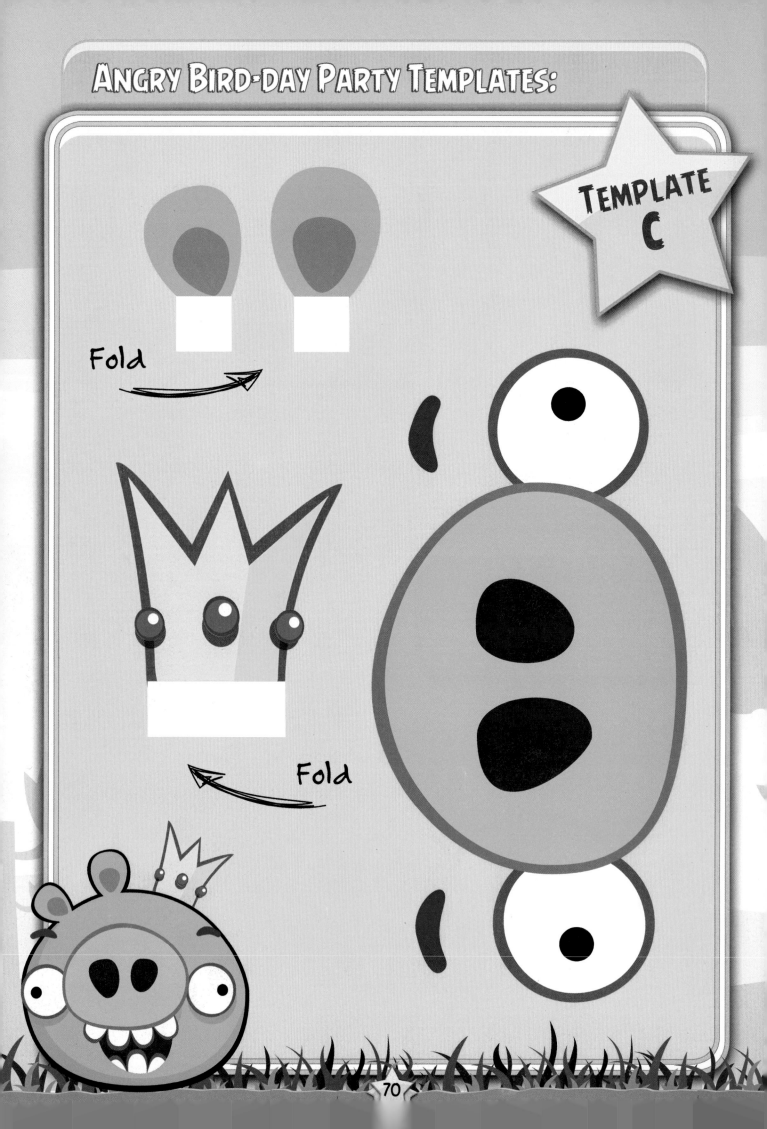

TEMPLATE C

Fold

Fold

Fold

TEMPLATE
D

CA-CAW, CA-CAKE!

You're sure to make an impression on your bird-loving chums with this crazy-cool cake which is oh so cross it's about to explode!

Make sure you scoff it first, or you'll be clearing icing from the walls for weeks!

FOR THE SPONGE:

HERE'S WHAT YOU DO:

1. Turn your oven to 180°C/gas mark 4 and grease the tins with butter.

2. Cream the butter and sugar together in a bowl.

3. Slowly add the beaten eggs.

4. Sieve the flour into the mixture and fold the mixture together.

5. Spoon mixture into cake tins.

6. Bake for 20 mins or until golden brown (when cooked a knife inserted into the centre should come out clean).

7. Leave to cool then turn out onto a cake board.

8. Spread one sponge generously with buttercream then place the other on top.

HERE'S WHAT YOU NEED:

- 175g unsalted butter
- 175g caster sugar
- 3 eggs (beaten)
- 175g self-raising flour (sieved)
- 2 x 20cm sandwich cake tins

SQUAWK!

Feathers will fly if you use the oven without permission!

Ask an adult to help in the kitchen!

FOR THE DECORATION:

HERE'S WHAT YOU NEED:
- Tracing paper
- Pencil
- Fondant icing in red, black, white and either yellow or orange
- One pot ready-made vanilla buttercream icing
- Warm water and a pastry brush

TEMPLATE

HERE'S WHAT YOU DO:

1. Using tracing paper, trace around the shapes below for the bird's features.

2. Roll out the red icing until it's big enough to cover the cake.

3. Brush the cake sparingly with warm water and cover the sponge with the icing.

4. Smooth the icing over the sponge and then trim around the edge.

5. Place the two head feather shapes onto the remaining red icing, cut round to create the head feathers and place at the top of the cake.

6. Roll out the white icing and cut a semi circle from it. Lay this over the bottom portion of the cake (as shown).

7. Place the eye shapes onto the white icing and cut round then place on the cake.

8. Place the beak shape onto the yellow or orange icing, cut round and place.

9. Do the same with the black icing and cut out the tail feathers and eyebrows. Place on the cake.

10. Finally roll two tiny balls from the black icing to make the bird's pupils. Lay them on the cake.

THE BIG BIRDIE QUIZ

PART 3

SPACE: THE FINAL FRONTIER AND THE FINAL DIMENSION OF OUR QUIZ. Can you cut it in another galaxy? Grab a pen and find out...

1 How have the birds and pigs ended up in Space?

2 How are the birds now dressed?

3 What colour does King Pig become when he is frozen?

4 What is different about a space egg, compared to a normal egg?

5 What form does the antenna on Major Pig's helmet take when in space?

6 Name two items of clothing the birds are seen with in space...

7 What does the Black Bird emit from the feathers on its head?

8 What shape is the Ice Bomb Bird?

9 Which colour is the bird who wears laser specs?

10 Name the bird which wears a black mask in space.

Go to **page 77** for all the answers

BIRDIE BYE BYE

We're so mad you dropped by.

See you later pig exterminator!

A message from Red...

Now you've collected all the letters, write them in the spaces below, in order, to make one of my favourite phrases!

ANSWERS

Pages 12 – 13: Picnic Panic

1. No
2. 3
3. Closed
4. A ham
5. The jug and a checked cloth/napkin
6. 4
7. On the right
8. Minions
9. In the picnic hamper
10. 6
11. Yellow and white
12. 1

Page 18-19: Spot the Difference

Page 30: Ode To A Bird

My feathers are **yellow**,
You'll be out of **luck**,
For my name is **Chuck**.

I look superb **in flight**
I **multiply!**
I'm **The Blues**.

I'm a bit of a **rotter**.
Commanding the **army**.
I'm **Corporal Pig**,

Pages 40-41: Spot The Piggy Pooper!

Pages 44-45: The Big Birdie Quiz Part 1

1. False, it's Red
2. True
3. False
4. False
5. False, his special power is triggerable acceleration. The Blues separate into three birds.
6. True
7. False. It's Matilda who does Nest Shui
8. False. It's Terence
9. False. He likes to sleep face down on the ground
10. No. Moustache Pig is the foreman. The helmeted pig is Colonel Pig and leads the army
11. True
12. False, they live on Piggy Island
13. False, they have three
14. False it's ca-caw!
15. True

Pages 50-51: Hide & Squeak

Page 58: In Space No One Can Hear You Oink!

Page 59: Space Search

O	C	A	P	I	A	N	N	T	E	N	A
O	I	C	I	A	S	T	R	O	D	S	S
M	A	E	B	R	E	G	A	L	V	E	T
O	S	W	E	E	E	E	W	O	H	C	E
M	T	M	L	S	G	Y	C	B	I	R	R
N	R	H	C	B	R	N	C	A	R	P	O
B	O	I	E	B	O	C	J	P	O	E	
U	C	T	R	U	R	B	E	E	O	R	D
I	D	O	Y	B	U	R	A	K	H	I	K
B	W	N	G	N	B	M	O	O	N	E	O
L	O	G	A	S	B	A	N	T	E	R	C
E	E	L	O	H	M	R	O	W	O	U	R

The extra hidden word is Superhero

Pages 62-63: The Big Birdie Quiz Part 2

1. b
2. a
3. c
4. c
5. c
6. a
7. a
8. b
9. b
10. c

Pages 74-75: The Big Birdie Quiz Part 3

1. They followed an alien bird and a metallic arm through a wormhole in the sky – to another galaxy
2. As superheroes
3. Blue
4. It has an antenna
5. It resembles a satellite dish
6. Capes, brooches, masks, specs/glasses
7. Flames
8. An ice cube
9. Lavender/lilac
10. Red

Page 76: Birdie Bye Bye

The letters you collected should spell out the phrase...

POP TWO PIGS WITH ONE BIRD